Practise your Phrasal Verbs

J B Heaton

Series editor: Donald Adamson

Longman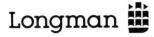

Longman Group Limited
Longman House, Burnt Mill, Harlow,
Essex. CM20 2JE England
and Associated Companies throughout the world.

First published 1995

Set in ITC Century Light

Produced through Longman Malaysia

ISBN 0 582 09667 7

Illustrated by David Farris, Shelagh McNicholas and
Robin Warburton

Acknowledgements
We are indebted to Longman Group Ltd for
permission to reproduce extracts from the *Longman*
Active Study Dictionary of English (1991)

Contents

Introduction

1 A phrasal verb is usually a two-word verb: e.g. *come back, fall off, find out, lie down, stand up.* The most common kind of phrasal verb is a VERB which is followed by an ADVERB. When it is part of a phrasal verb, this adverb is called a PARTICLE.

For example:

Verb	+	Particle	=	Phrasal verb
throw		away		throw away

2 A particle is usually an ADVERB: e.g.

about, along, around, away, back, by, down, in, off, on, out, over, round, up

Sometimes it simply **adds** to the meaning of a verb:
When I *turned round*, I saw Ann behind me.
or it can completely **change** the meaning of a verb:
A car suddenly *pulled up* behind me. (= came to a stop)

3 A particle can also be a PREPOSITION which goes very closely with the verb and which changes the meaning of the verb.

Have you *come across* my old exercise book in the store room? (= found)
Your new red tie doesn't *go with* your yellow shirt. (= match)

The phrasal verbs used in exercises 4 and 5 are listed below.

Verb	+	Particle	=	Phrasal verb
clear		up		clear up (= solve)
come		back		come back
find		out		find out (= discover, learn)
get		back		get back (= return)
get		on		get on (= manage)
get		up		get up (= rise, get out of bed)
go		away		go away
pick		up		pick up
pull		up		pull up (= stop)
run		off		run off
set		off		set off (= start a journey)
take		out		take out
throw		away		throw away
turn		up		turn up (= arrive, appear)
wear		out		wear out (= exhaust, tire)

4 Read the newspaper article on the right and circle the phrasal verbs in it.

Be careful not to circle a verb followed by an **ordinary** preposition which does **not** change the meaning of a verb in any way and which goes with the following noun, e.g. *dating from the 13th century (from =* preposition)

Modern-day thieves pick up the habits of the past

In modern-day York, thieves often throw away empty purses and wallets. By observing this habit, archaeologists have cleared up a mystery.

"We often wondered why there were so many empty purses dating from the 13th century on this site," one of the archaeologists said. "Then suddenly we found out why."

Mr Nick Pearson, the senior archaeologist said to reporters yesterday: "Every Monday when we came back to the site after going away for the weekend, we found empty purses and wallets which had been thrown over the fence round the site.

They had obviously been stolen from people in the area. The thieves had run off and taken out the credit cards and cash. They didn't want the purses and wallets, so they threw them away. It seems that criminals haven't changed much in 700 years!"

5 Read the letter below and find phrasal verbs which mean the same as the verbs underneath. The synonyms are in the same order as the phrasal verbs used in the letter.

Dear Susie,

I hope you got on all right when you went to London last week.

Yesterday I went on a school picnic. I got up very early and then met my friends. We waited for over an hour before the coach turned up. We found out later that the coach had set off half an hour late. The driver was in such a hurry that he almost crashed into a car on the way. Luckily, he pulled up just in time. Then half-way to the beach we had a puncture. What a day! We were all worn out and angry when we at last got back home.

Write soon.

Love,
Mary

1 managed	_got on_	5 started	_____
2 arose	_____	6 stopped	_____
3 arrived	_____	7 were tired	_____
4 discovered	_____	8 returned	_____

1 Recognising phrasal verbs (1)

Sometimes a particle can simply add to the meaning of a verb rather than changing it. In such cases, it is easy to guess the meaning of the phrasal verb (i.e. the verb and the particle together).

These are the verbs used in this unit:

come back	fly away	go past	shout out
come down	get in	look up	turn round
come over	get out	run off	wake up
fall down	get up		

1 Complete the sentences, using a suitable phrasal verb from the list below.

come back   come over   get out   go past   turn round

1   Look at that new car ____going____ _past_ .

2   What's happening? It's _____ _____

3   and it's _____ _____ .

4   The car's stopping and the driver's _____ _____ .

5   He's _____ _____ to talk to us.

I think he's lost his way.

2 Complete this story, using a suitable phrasal verb (in the correct tense) from the list below.

get out	come back	wake up	run off	get in	shout out	get up

Last night I left my bedroom window open, and a burglar managed to

1 ____get____ ___in___ . When he was near my bed, he made a noise,

and I ²_____ _____ and ³_____ _____ . The burglar

at once ran to the window to ⁴_____ _____ . I think he hurt

himself as he fell on the path outside but he ⁵_____ _____ and

⁶_____ _____ . I don't think he will ⁷_____ _____ !

3 Here are the answers to some questions. Look at each picture below and then complete the questions. Try to use one of the phrasal verbs in the list at the beginning of this unit.

1   Why _____is the bus going past_____ without stopping?
Because it's full.

2   Why _____ ?
Because there isn't enough air in it.

3   Why _____ ?
Because someone's left the cage door open.

4   Why _____ ?
Because someone is shouting at him.

5   Why _____ ?
Because there's a bee above her head.

> Sometimes it is difficult to guess the meaning of a phrasal verb because the particle gives the verb a NEW MEANING.
>
> Our bus was held up by the fog. (*held up* = DELAYED)

In this unit you will learn to identify phrasal verbs of this type and their meanings from dictionary entries, and by doing exercises on the phrasal verbs listed.

1 Read this page from a dictionary and then complete the sentences below with a suitable phrasal verb. Write the correct form of the verb in the longer blank and the particle in the shorter blank.

hold sthg **against** sbdy *phr v* [T] to continue to feel angry with someone or dislike them because of something bad that they did in the past: *The fact that someone has been in prison should not be held against them.*

hold back *phr v* **1** [T hold sbdy/sthg ↔ **back**] to prevent someone or something from moving forwards: *Police held the crowd back.* | *People built banks of earth to hold back the flood waters.* **2** [I] to be unwilling to do something because you are not sure that it is the right thing to do: *She held back for a long time before she finally went to the police.* **3** [T hold sbdy ↔ **back**] to prevent someone from developing properly: *Illness can hold a child back quite significantly.* **4** [T hold sthg ↔ **back**] to keep something secret: *I knew that he was holding something back.*

hold sthg ↔ **down** *phr v* [T] **1** to keep a job: *He seems to be unable to hold down a job for more than a few weeks.* **2** to keep something at a low level: *the government's determination to hold down prices.*

hold forth *phr v* [T] *fml* to talk for a long time about something

hold sbdy/sthg ↔ **off** *phr v* [T] to cause someone or something to remain at a distance: *They managed to hold off the enemy's attack.*

hold on *phr v* [I] *infml* to wait for a short time: *Could you hold on? I'll just see if he's in.*

hold onto sthg *phr v* [T] **1** to hold something with your hand: *She held onto the side of the boat.* **2** to manage to keep something: *He held onto his job.*

hold out *phr v* **1** [T hold sthg ↔ **out**] to offer something to someone by moving it towards them: *He held out his hand to her.* **2** [I] to manage to last in spite of difficulties: *The people held out until help arrived.* **3** hold out hope to remain hopeful: *I don't hold out much hope that the weather will improve.*

hold out for sthg *phr v* [T] to demand something firmly and wait until you get it: *The men are still holding out for more pay.*

hold sthg **over** *phr v* [T] to move something to a later date: *We may have to hold the meeting over until next week.*

hold sbdy **to** sthg *phr v* [T] to make someone do what they said that they would do: *I shall hold him to his promise.*

hold up *phr v* **1** [T hold sbdy/sthg ↔ **up**] to delay someone or something: *The building work was held up by the bad weather.* **2** [T hold sbdy ↔ **up**] to stop someone in order to rob them: *He was held up at gunpoint and robbed.* **3** [hold sbdy/sthg ↔ **up**] to give someone or something as an example of something: *He always held up his youngest son as a model of hard work.*

hold with sthg *phr v* [T] **not hold with something** to not agree with something: *I don't hold with these modern teaching methods.*

(*Longman Active Study Dictionary of English*)

1 The soldiers were determined to _____hold_____ ___out___ against the enemy as long as they possibly could.

2 The government was successful in _____ _____ inflation, and there was no increase in either prices or wages for over a year.

3 I'm very sorry we're late. We were _____ _____ by all the traffic.

4 _____ _____ a moment. I'll look up the word in a dictionary and tell you its exact meaning. It won't take me long.

5 I think Sue's _____ something _____ . I don't know what it is, but I don't think she's told us everything she knows about the accident.

6 They've decided to _____ _____ the whole matter until January.

7 The armed gang rushed into the building and _____ _____ everyone in the bank.

2 Which headline (A–F) goes with which article (1–6)? Write the correct letter beside each article. Use the dictionary extract and the phrasal verbs below to help you.

1 ——
> The government will announce its new employment policy tomorrow. It plans to create at least 100,000 more jobs in the north of the country.

A
> ### Government fails to put across policy

2 ——
> Research has shown that nowadays most people over the age of sixty have saved hardly any money at all. Only two people in every hundred have enough to keep them for the rest of their lives.

B
> ### Put money by for old age

3 ——
> A giant international sports stadium, two Olympic swimming-pools and ten indoor tennis courts will be built on the outskirts of Bonham City, according to the Minister for Sports.

C
> ### Government puts down rebellion

4 ——
> The military government has postponed handing over to a democratic civilian government for a further six months. Instead of being held on May 15, as planned, voting will now take place at the end of November.

D
> ### Government puts off elections

5 ——
> An attempt to overthrow the Government of Mobishu failed last week when the government army defeated several thousand rebels after fierce fighting outside the capital.

E
> ### Government puts out job creation policy

6 ——
> The government has been criticised for failing to explain fully and clearly its attitude towards cigarette advertising. Many people are confused about whether it intends to ban all advertisements or only limit the number.

F
> ### Sports centre to be put up

---

put across	put by	put down	put off	put out	put up

---

put sthg ↔ **across** *phr v* [T] to explain something so that people can understand it: *She didn't succeed in putting her ideas across very well.*

put sthg ↔ **by** *phr v* [T] to save money so that you can use it later: *I've got a bit of money put by for my old age.*

put down *phr v* **1** [T put sthg ↔ down] to defeat a protest, usually by using force: *Troops were called in to help put down the rebellion.* **2** [T put sbdy ↔ down] *infml* to make someone feel ashamed or foolish **3** [T put sthg ↔ down] to kill an animal, usually because it is old or ill: *Two horses had to be put down after the race.*

put sbdy **down for** sthg *phr v* [T] to put someone's name on a list of people who are going to do something

put sthg **down to** sbdy/sthg *phr v* [T] to say or think that something was caused by a particular person or thing: *He didn't look well but I just put it down to the fact that he was tired.*

put off *phr v* **1** [T put sthg ↔ off] to delay something until a later date: *The meeting's been put off until next month.* **2** [T put sbdy ↔ off] to tell someone that you cannot do something that you had agreed to do: *We're expecting them for dinner, but we'll have to put them off because the children aren't well.* **3** [T put sbdy off sbdy/sthg)] to make someone feel that they no longer like a person or thing, or that they no longer want to do something: *My first week at university put me off university life completely.* | *Don't tell him all the unpleasant aspects of the work – you'll put him off.*

put out *phr v* **1** [T put sthg ↔ out] to broadcast or print official information: *The government will put out a new statement on the economy tomorrow.* **2** [T put sthg ↔ out] to stop a fire from burning **3** [T put sthg ↔ out] to stop a light from shining: *Don't forget to put the lights out when you leave.* **4** [T put sbdy out] to trouble or annoy someone: *I felt somewhat put out by his behaviour.* **5 put yourself out** to take

trouble and make an effort to do something: *He'll never put himself out to help anyone.*

put up *phr v* **1** [T put sthg ↔ up] to build or raise something: *They're going to put up 20 new houses here.* | *I've never put up a tent on my own.* | *She put up her umbrella.* **2** [T put sthg ↔ up] to put a notice in a public paper: *The exam results will be put up on the main notice board.* | *They put up posters advertising the meeting.* **3** [T put sthg ↔ up] to increase a cost or price: *Most companies are expected to put their prices up by about 10% this year.* **4** [T put sbdy ↔ up] to give someone food and lodging: *Will you be able to put me up tonight?* **5 put up a fight, put up resistance** to struggle to avoid something happening to you: *Local groups are putting up a lot of resistance to the scheme.* | *In the end he was arrested without putting up much of a fight.* **6 put something up for sale** to offer something for sale: *She's decided to put her house up for sale.*

(Longman Active Study Dictionary of English)

3 Word order (1): noun objects

Most phrasal verbs are two-word verbs which can take noun objects either
BEFORE or AFTER the particle.

EITHER	**verb**	+	**noun phrase**	+	**particle**
	Bring		a friend		*along.*
She	*gave*		all the books		*out.*

OR	**verb**	+	**particle**	+	**noun phrase**
	Bring		*along*		a friend.
She	*gave*		*out*		all the books.

Note
If the noun phrase is quite long, the particle usually comes
immediately after the verb.

1 Rewrite the instructions, using the particle in brackets. At (a) put the particle after
the noun or noun phrase and at (b) place it immediately after the verb.

How to use your new camera

1 Open the back of the camera and put the film.   (in)

(a) <u>Open the back of the camera and put the film in.</u>

(b) <u>Open the back of the camera and put in the film.</u>

2 Don't throw the small container for the film.   (away)

(a) _____

(b) _____

3 Wind the film until Number 1 appears in the window.   (on)

(a)

(b) _____

4 When you have finished, wind all the film.   (back)

(a) _____

(b)

5 Open your camera and take the film.   (out)

(a) _____

(b) _____

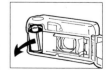

6 Send the film to be developed and printed.   (off)

(a) _____

(b) _____

2 Your friend doesn't hear your questions. Repeat each question at the end of the short conversations below.

1 A: Put the magazines down.
  B: Which magazines?
  A: The magazines which you're holding.
  B: I didn't hear what you said.
  A: *Will you put down the magazines which you're holding?*

2 A: Now pick that magazine up.
  B: Which magazine do you mean?
  A: The magazine on the top of the pile.
  B: Would you mind saying that again?

  A: _____

3 A: Cut the first page out.
  B: Which is the first page?
  A: The page with the big advertisement on it.
  B: Sorry. I don't understand what you want me to do.

  A: _____

4 A: Now hold the advertisement up.
  B: What advertisement?
  A: The advertisement on the page that you've just cut out.
  B: I'm not sure I heard you correctly.

  A: _____

  _____

3 Each line of the paragraph below has the particle missing from the phrasal verb. Draw a line (/) to show where the particle should go and write the particle above. Sometimes there may be more than one correct position for the particle.

1 Something caught Katie's attention. She bent *down* / and   (down)

2 picked a small envelope addressed to her sister. She saw a   (up)

3 wooden seat nearby and sat. Then she decided to   (down)

4 find what was inside the envelope. She opened it,   (out)

5 put her hand and felt something small and hard. She slowly   (in)

6 took a shining object. It was a gold watch!   (out)

④ Word order (2): pronoun objects

When the object of a phrasal verb is a PRONOUN (*it*, *me*, *him*, *them*, etc.), it must always be put BEFORE the particle.

	verb	+	pronoun	+	particle
Pick up all the paper and	*throw*		*it*		*away.*
Sue took some books out of the cupboard and	*gave*		*them*		*out.*

1 Answer the questions below, using a suitable phrasal verb from the list and a pronoun.

take off   send out   pick up   button up   put out   give out   blow up   fill in

1

What's Ali doing with the cat?
He's picking it up.

5

What's Adam doing with the form?
_____

2

What's Dave doing with the balloon?
_____

6

What's Mrs Lee doing with the two boys?
_____

3

What's Fatimah doing with her shoes?
_____

7

What's Anna doing with her coat?
_____

4

What's Mr Sabri doing with his cigarette?
_____

8

What's Sam doing with the books?
_____

2 Read the conversation below and rewrite B's replies in the correct order.

A: Did anyone take my bag?
B: up / Tom / it / picked / Yes,
   Yes, Tom picked it up.

A: I wonder what he did with it.
B: put / down / He / it / somewhere

_____

A: Here it is, but there's a pen missing.
B: probably / it / out / to/ took / He / use/ it

_____

A: Well, it isn't here. I wonder where it is.
B: out / have / must / It / fallen

_____

A: I can't see it anywhere here.
B: hope / taken / I / has / away / it / no one

_____

3 What did these people do? Write sentences, using a suitable phrasal verb
(in the correct tense) from the list below.

1  2  3  4

| try on | spit out | tear up | lock up |

1 What did Ken do after he'd read the
  letter?
  He tore it up.

2 What did Mrs Chen do after the assistant
  took the hat out of the window?

  _____

3 What did the police do when they caught
  the thief?

  _____

4 What did Shirley do after she'd tasted the
  medicine?

  _____

5 Particles and prepositions

When ADVERBS are used as particles, they can come either BEFORE or AFTER a noun object:

EITHER	**verb**	+	**noun phrase**	+	**particle**	
	Look		the word		up	in the dictionary.

OR	**verb**	+	**particle**	+	**noun phrase**	
	Look		up		the word	in the dictionary.

However, adverb particles always come AFTER a pronoun object:

	verb	+	**pronoun**	+	**particle**	
	Look		it		up	in the dictionary.

When PREPOSITIONS are used as particles, they always come BEFORE a noun object or a pronoun object:

	verb	+	**particle**	+	**noun phrase**
Who's	looking		after		the babies?

	verb	+	**particle**	+	**pronoun**
Who's	looking		after		them?

Note
We **cannot** say 'Who's looking the babies after?'

1 Study the following phrases:

wait for something	(*for* = preposition)
fill something with water	(*with* = preposition)
pour something in something else	(*in* = preposition)
put something in something else	(*in* = preposition)
plug something in	(*in* = adverb)
rinse something out	(*out* = adverb)
sit down	(*down* = adverb)
switch something on/off	(*on/off* = adverb)

The paragraph below has several particles missing from the phrasal verbs. Draw a line (/) to show where each particle should go, and write the adverb or preposition above.

with
First, fill an electric kettle / water and plug it. Next get a teapot and

rinse it with hot water from the kettle. Then put a tea-bag the teapot.

As soon as the kettle boils, switch it and pour the boiling water the teapot.

After a few minutes fill your cup tea, put some milk and sugar if you like,

sit and enjoy your tea. Don't wait anyone or your tea will get cold!

2 Study the following phrases:

bring something in/into a place	(*in/into* = preposition)
look at something	(*at* = preposition)
write something on a page	(*on* = preposition)
write over something	(*over* = preposition)
copy something out	(*out* = adverb)
cross something out	(*out* = adverb)
rub something out	(*out* = adverb)
take something out	(*out* = adverb)
turn something over	(*over* = adverb)

Now read the teacher's instructions for the exam below and write answers to the students' questions underneath.

You may write notes on the last page but you should cross out all your rough work when you have finished. Write neatly, but try not to waste time copying out your answers. Don't try to rub out your mistakes. If you make a mistake, cross out a word and write it out again. If you make so many mistakes that it is difficult to read your answer, cross out the whole sentence and start again. You must put away any books you have brought into the room with you.

1 What about writing on the last page?   You can write on it.

2 How about crossing out our rough work?   _____

3 Should we copy out our answers?   _____

4 What should we do about rubbing out our mistakes?   _____

5 And crossing out any wrong words?   _____

6 And the same with a whole sentence?   _____

7 Can you tell us anything about bringing books into the room?   _____

8 What do you think about looking at our books in the exam?   _____

6 Revision (1)

1 Rewrite the following sentences. At (a) begin the sentence with *Someone* and at (b) begin the sentence with *I wonder who*.

1 The television has been taken away.

(a) Someone has taken the television away.

(b) I wonder who has taken it away?

2 One of the wires has been pulled out.

(a) _____

(b) _____

3 The CD you asked for has just been brought back.

(a) _____

(b) _____

4 The last two pages of the book have been torn out.

(a) _____

(b) _____

5 The painting the committee didn't like has now been taken down.

(a) _____

(b) _____

6 The instructions the teacher wrote on the blackboard have been rubbed out.

(a) _____

(b) _____

2 Read the extract from a dictionary and complete the following sentences with a phrasal verb which has the same meaning as the word or words in brackets.

(Longman Active Study Dictionary of English)

bring in *phr v* [T **bring** sthg ↔ **in**] to introduce something: *The government is bringing in new laws to protect children.* **2** [T **bring** sbdy ↔ **in**] to ask someone to take part in something, especially in order to help with a problem: *We need to bring in a few experienced people to get the job finished on time.* **3** [T **bring** sthg ↔ **in**] to earn a particular amount of money: *She's bringing in £200 a week.* | *This new tax will bring in a lot of extra money for the government.*
bring sthg ↔ **off** *phr v* [T] to succeed in doing something difficult: *It will be a great achievement if they manage to bring it off.*
bring on *phr v* **1** [T **bring** sbdy/sthg ↔ **on**] to cause someone or something to grow, develop, or improve: *The shock nearly brought on a heart attack.* | *He was given special coaching to bring him on.* **1 bring something on yourself** to cause something unpleasant to happen to you
bring out *phr v* **1** [T **bring** sthg ↔ **out**] to produce a new product: *The company has just brought out a new range of cosmetics.* **1 bring out the best in someone** to make someone behave very well: *The crisis brought out the best in everyone.* [RELATED PHRASE: **bring out the worst in someone**] **3** [T **bring** sbdy **out**] to encourage someone to talk to other people and feel at ease with other people
bring ↔ **round** *phr v* [T] **1** to cause someone to regain consciousness: *We tried everything we could think of to bring her round.* **2** to persuade someone to change their opinion so that it is the same as your opinion
bring up *phr v* **1** [T **bring** sbdy ↔ **up**] to educate and care for a child: *I think that both parents should be involved in bringing up the children.* | *She was a polite and well brought up child.* –see RAISE[1] (USAGE) **2** [T **bring** sthg ↔ **up**] to introduce a subject during a conversation: *I didn't dare bring up the question of money.* | *All these problems were brought up at the last meeting.* **3** [T **bring** sthg ↔ **up**] to be sick: *He ate his dinner and then promptly brought it all up again.*

1 I hope getting so wet doesn't _____ a cold or a fever.   (cause)

2 We were having a pleasant conversation when he suddenly _____ the subject of our previous quarrel.   (introduced)

3 Give Susie a teaspoonful of this medicine. It should soon _____ her _____ .   (help her to regain consciousness)

4 The transport minister wants to _____ a new system for reducing the number of cars in city centres.   (introduce)

5 Charles disagreed with me at first but we eventually _____ him _____ , and I'm sure he'll vote with us now.   (persuaded him to agree with my opinion)

6 Tourism has succeeded in _____ over a hundred million dollars so far this year.   (earning)

7 When is the company going to _____ the new car on which they've been working so long?   (produce)

8 Did the new manager _____ the important business deal with the Japanese company?   (succeed in accomplishing)

3 Each line of the letter below has a particle or preposition missing. Draw a line (/) to show where it should go and write the particle or the preposition in the space at the side.

Dear Wendy

I am sorry I missed you yesterday. I didn't get/until nine o'clock and, although I set from home at half past nine, you had left when I arrived. I do hope you didn't wait me.

I am very disappointed because I wanted to talk you and look your old photographs.

To make matters worse, I took me some of my own photographs but I lost them on the way to meet you. I was looking them on the bus and I remember putting them when I opened my purse and took my money to pay my fare.

Someone must have seen my photographs and picked them. I only hope they haven't thrown them.

I look forward to getting a letter or phone call you soon.

Love,

Mary

1 __up__
2 _____
3 _____
4 _____
5 _____
6 _____
7 _____
8 _____
9 _____
10 _____
11 _____
12 _____

7 *In, out*

1

in =	INWARDS, TOWARDS THE MIDDLE
	The wall *curves in* at each end.
	His left foot *turned in* as he walked.
out =	OUTWARDS, AWAY FROM THE TOP OR SIDE OF SOMETHING
	The wall *curves out* at each end.
	Be careful. There's a sharp nail *sticking out*.

| hang out | jut out | stick out |
| bend in/out | curve in/out | turn in/out |

Look at the pictures of the two cars.

Which car does each sentence describe (A or B)?

1 The bonnet of the car curves in at the front. _____A_____

2 The boot sticks out a long way. _____

3 There's something hanging out at the back of the car. _____

4 There are some tail lights jutting out at the back of

the car. _____

5 Both the front and back of the car curve in. _____

6 There are two wing mirrors sticking out on the bonnet. _____

7 The dashboard is dangerous because parts of it stick out. _____

8 The top of the aerial at the back bends out. _____

2

in =	FROM ALL DIRECTIONS (TO THE CENTRE) OR FROM SEVERAL PEOPLE
	Have all the pupils *handed in* their examination papers?
out =	IN ALL DIRECTIONS OR TO SEVERAL PEOPLE
	Will you help the teacher to *give out* the exercise books?

| come in/out | give sthg in/out | pour (sthg) in/out | bring sthg/sbdy in |
| go in/out | hand sthg in/out | send sthg/sbdy in/out | take sthg/sbdy out |

Complete the paragraph, using a suitable phrasal verb from the list on page 18. Although there is more than one correct answer in most cases, you should not use the same verb twice.

People [1]_____hand_____ _in_ all kinds of things at a lost property office. Recently someone even [2]_____ _____ a small elephant! Every day hundreds of enquiries [3]_____ _____ about articles which people have lost or mislaid. If no one has [4]_____ _____ the articles concerned, the lost property office will [5]_____ _____ descriptions to all the other lost property offices in the area.

Now rewrite the paragraph above, using each verb in the passive **if possible**.

All kinds of things have been handed in at lost
property offices. Recently a small elephant
_____
_____
_____
_____
_____
_____

3 Complete this paragraph with suitable phrasal verbs from the list in exercise 2.

Over 20,000 application forms for the chess competition have been [1]_____sent_____ _out_ . They were posted during the last three days. In addition, 2,000 forms were [2]_____ _____ yesterday by people standing in busy shopping centres, and so it appears that the competition will be a great success. Completed forms are already beginning to [3]_____ _____ . All forms should be [4]_____ _____ , using the stamped addressed envelopes provided. Forms should not be [5]_____ _____ personally to this office: there are not enough staff to deal with them.

8 *Off, on* (1)

off	=	SEPARATED, DETACHED FROM
		I can't open the door now. Who *broke* the handle *off*?
on	=	ATTACHED TO, PART OF
		Can you *glue* the doll's hand *on*?

break sthg off	fall off	put sthg on	stay on
come off	pull sthg off	screw sthg on	stick sthg on
cut sthg off	take sthg off	sew sthg on	tie sthg on

1 Fill in the blanks with verbs from the list below and *on* or *off*.

stay stick screw put pull tie take sew break come

1 A: Oh dear. One of my buttons has ¹___*come*___ *off* .

   B: Don't worry. I've got a needle and thread. I can

     ²_____ it _____ for you.

2 A: Oh no! I've knocked this jug and the handle has

     ³_____ _____ .

   B: Try using this glue to ⁴_____ it _____ .

3 A: Someone's ⁵_____ the door handle _____ .

   B: Don't worry. I'll ⁶_____ it _____ again.

4 A: What do I do after I've ⁷_____ this wheel _____ ?

   B: Take the spare wheel out of the boot and ⁸_____

     that _____ .

5 A: The lid won't ⁹_____ _____ the container.

   B: Why don't you ¹⁰_____ it _____ ?

2

off	=	DISCONNECT OR TURN SO THAT IT IS NOT WORKING
		Please *switch* the light *off* when you leave the room.
on	=	CONNECT OR TURN SO THAT IT IS WORKING
		Who's *turned on* this tap?

Use the table below to help you answer the questions.

Check Make sure that	something	is switched is turned is	on off
Leave Turn Switch	something		

Imagine you are going to leave your house or flat for ten days.

1 What would you do about the cooker?

   I would turn _it off_____ .

2 What would you do about the heating if the weather was very cold?

   I would leave _____ .

3 What would you do about the air-conditioner if the weather was hot?

   I would make sure that _____ .

4 What would you do about all the lights?

   I would turn _____ .

5 What would you do about all the taps?

   I would check _____ .

Now imagine you are going to leave your house or flat for only ten minutes.

6 What would you do about the air-conditioner if the weather was
   very hot?

   I would _____ .

7 What would you do about the lights? Would you switch them all off?

   I would _____ .

8 What would you do about the food you were cooking in the oven?

   I would _____ .

9 What would you do about your video recorder if you wanted to see a
   programme which started in the next five minutes?

   I would _____ .

10 What would you do about your computer if you were working on it at
    the time?

    I would _____ .

9 Off, on (2)

off =	REMOVING CLOTHES
	Please come in and *take* your hat and coat *off*.
on =	WEARING CLOTHES
	Put on some thick gloves. It's very cold today.

Note: to *help* someone *on* with clothes = to help them put clothes on

get sthg on/off	leave sthg on/off	put sthg on	take sthg off
help sbdy on/off	pull on/off	slip on/off	try on

Fill in the blanks in the conversation below, using a suitable phrasal verb from the list above.

A: I'd like a pair of brown shoes, please. Just like those on the shelf over there.

B: Certainly, sir. What size are the shoes you've ¹__*got*__ __*on*__ now?

A: I'm not certain.

B: Well, why don't you ²_____ your shoes _____ and let me measure your feet.

   Hold your foot straight out, sir. Ah, you'll need size 8 shoes. Would you like to

   ³_____ this pair _____ and see if they're comfortable?

A: All right. Have you got a shoe horn?

B: There's one here, sir, but I'll ⁴_____ you _____ with them.

A: Oh dear! They seem far too small.

B: ⁵_____ them _____ a moment and walk a few yards on the carpet. How do

   they feel when you walk in them?

A: Terrible. They make my feet hurt. Oh dear, my feet seem to be stuck in them!

B: Leave it to me. I'm very strong. Just hold your right foot out and I'll

   ⁶_____ the shoe _____ , sir.

A: Ow! . . . .

2

> cut someone off = turn the power off
> let someone off = allow them to go unpunished
> put something off = delay something till a later date
> call something off = decide not to go ahead with something
> break (a friendship/working relations) off = stop seeing/working with someone

Complete the sentences below, using a phrasal verb which means the same as the word or words in italics.

1 Mr Asano asked if they could _____ the meeting _____ until Friday. The committee agreed and so the meeting was *postponed*.

2 The players wanted to _____ the match _____ but the manager refused. However, as the storm got worse, he finally decided to *cancel* it.

3 We received a letter from the electricity company threatening to *disconnect* us unless we paid our bill. Unfortunately we didn't pay and so we were

_____ _____ .

4 Our company finally decided to _____ _____ relations with our business partners in America. We had to *stop working together* because of differences of opinion.

5 The judge gave the thief a warning and _____ him _____ . The thief was amazed that he *wasn't punished*.

3 Complete Maria's letter, using a suitable phrasal verb from the list in exercise 2.

Dear Anna,
   I am writing to you as we always seem to get _____
_____ whenever we talk to each other on the phone. Anyway,
I'm afraid I have to _____ _____ our visit to the cinema as I
have been asked to look after my baby brother that evening. Can
we possibly _____ it _____ until the end of the week?
   I was glad to hear that you were not fined for parking outside
the city hall last week. I felt sure the police would _____ you
_____ when you explained everything to them.
   This must be all for now. I do hope we can arrange to go out
another evening, especially as I feel very lonely now that I have
_____ _____ with Jerry.
                              Love, Maria

10 *Down*, *up* (1)

down	=	FROM A HIGHER TO A LOWER PLACE OR LEVEL, TOWARDS THE GROUND
		The sun will *go down* in an hour.
		Put your books *down* and come here.
down	=	INTO A LOWER BODY POSITION
		I'm going to *lie down* for a few minutes.
up	=	FROM A LOWER TO A HIGHER PLACE OR LEVEL, AWAY FROM THE GROUND
		Is this lift *going up*?
		Can you help me *hang* the picture *up*?
up	=	INTO A HIGHER BODY POSITION, UPRIGHT
		Everyone *stood up* when the principal entered the room.

bend down	pick sthg up	stand up
go down/up	put sthg down/up	straighten up
jump up (and down)	sit down/up	take sthg down/up
kneel down	walk down/up	

Look at the pictures on the right and complete the story, using one of the phrasal verbs from the list above.

As soon as Susan reached the entrance to the block of flats where Dave lived, she ¹___put___ the case ___down___ . A moment later the lift door opened and out stepped Dave. After warmly greeting her, he ²_____ her case _____ . 'My flat's on the third floor, but there may not be enough room for both of us in the lift,' he said.

'If you take my case in the lift, I'll ³_____ ,' Susan said. When the lift reached the third floor, Dave ⁴_____ to pick the case up. Then he cried out in pain and ⁵_____ . As soon as he caught sight of Susan, however, he tried to ⁶_____ . But it was no use! Realising that he had hurt his back, Susan ⁷_____ to see what the matter was. '⁸_____ here,' she said to Dave after she had brought a chair for him. 'I'll get a doctor.'

2 Complete the conversation, using the most suitable verb from the list below and *down* or *up*.

> bend   pick   put   stand   take

A: This wall looks very bare. Why have you [1] _taken_ all your pictures _down_ ?

B: I'm changing them. I want to [2]_____ new ones _____ , but my back still hurts.

I'm afraid I can't [3]_____ _____ to [4]_____ anything _____ .

A: I'll help you. Just [5]_____ _____ and I'll pass the pictures to you.

3 Write an answer to each question below, using verbs from this list.

> make up a story = invent
> let someone down = fail, disappoint
> bring up children = educate, care for
>
> turn up = arrive, appear
> break down = fail, stop working
> pull down (a building) = demolish

1 Mr Johnson has promised to attend an important meeting but he isn't there. You know that he was coming in an old car he had just bought. What do you think has happened?

His car has probably broken down.

2 Tom was only two when his parents were killed in a road accident. His nearest relative was his grandmother. What do you think happened to him?

_____

3 There is a plan to build a new supermarket where the old cinema now stands. What will happen to the cinema before the supermarket can be built?

_____

4 Your friend says he will help you to do something, but he never appears. How do you feel?

_____

5 Peter asks you to lend him some money. He tells you that he has to pay for his father to go into hospital. However, you have just seen his father playing tennis and he looks very healthy. Do you think Peter is telling the truth or not?

_____

6 You have been asked to go to a very important meeting, but you know it will be very boring. Nevertheless, you will be able to help your friend at the meeting. What will you do?

_____

11 *Down*, *up* (2)

1

> *down* = TO A LOWER LEVEL IN PRICE, QUANTITY, AMOUNT, LOUDNESS, etc.
> Prices have *come down*.
> Can you please *turn* the radio *down*?
>
> *up* = TO A HIGHER LEVEL IN PRICE, QUANTITY, AMOUNT, LOUDNESS, etc.
> They've *put* all their prices *up* in that shop.
> I can't hear you. Please *speak up*!

be down	be up
come down (in price)	creep up
bring (prices, etc.) down	go up (in price)
force (prices, etc.) down	put (prices, etc.) up
quieten sbdy down	shoot up
shout sbdy down	step up (production, etc.)
turn (the volume, etc.) down	turn (the volume, etc.) up

Complete the paragraph with a suitable phrasal verb which has the same meaning as
the word in brackets.

Apples were 60 cents a kilo last week, but they have now ¹___*gone up*___ (risen)
by 20 cents a kilo. Mangoes have ²_____ (fallen) in price by 10 cents from
last week. The price of lemons has also been ³_____ (reduced), but
limes have been ⁴_____ (increased) to 40 cents a kilo. The large number
of oranges imported from Spain has ⁵_____ (reduced) their price.

2 Fill in the blanks with *down* or *up*.

1 Can you quieten the children __*down*__ so that I can hear myself speaking?

2 This record is too loud. Please turn the volume _____ .

3 If the picture on the screen is too dark, turn the brightness control _____ .

4 When the speaker tried to address the meeting, the audience angrily shouted
   him _____ .

5 Everything seems to cost a lot more this year. I wonder why prices have gone _____ .

6 It's a good time to buy computers now. They've come _____ by 50%.

7 The new factory is doing very well and has stepped _____ production as a result of
   a large order from abroad.

8 Food prices never shot _____ : they crept _____ gradually and at first no one
   realised the extent of inflation.

3 Look at the graph below and then complete the paragraph, using a suitable verb from the list and *down* or *up*.

stepped   came   crept   forced   shot

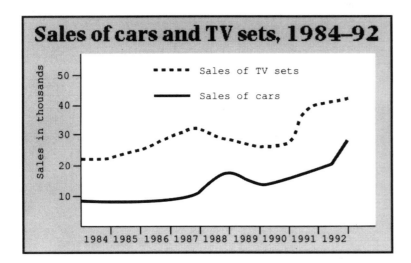

Sales of cars and TV sets, 1984–92

The number of small cars sold between 1984 and 1987 remained roughly the same. However, sales suddenly [1] *shot* *up* during the first half of 1988 but [2]_____ _____ a little in the following year. Since the end of 1989, however, the number of cars sold [3]_____ _____ steadily until January 1992. That month, however, Nikam [4]_____ _____ production of their cheaper models and [5]_____ _____ the prices of most other imported cars. As a result of the fall in prices, car sales rose sharply again.

4 Now use the information in the graph to write a few sentences describing the sale of TV sets between 1984 and 1993.

_____
_____
_____
_____
_____
_____
_____
_____

12 *Up* (1)

1

up	=	NOT IN BED
		I *got up* very late this morning.
		Was Dave *up* when you called?
		Don't *wait up* for me. I may be late. (= wait for someone instead of going to bed)

be up	get up	stay up	wait up

Complete the sentences to describe each picture.

1  2  3

1 He _____ to watch the match on TV.

2 The boy _____ yet.

3 He knows that it's time to _____ .

2

up	=	INTO SMALL PIECES
		I decided to *tear* the letter *up* and start again.

break up	cut up	divide up	chop up	dig up	tear up

Complete the sentences, using a suitable verb from the list above.

1 I felt so angry that I *tore up the letter.* _____

2 The workmen have started to _____

3 Let's make a model castle; we can _____

4 We can all have a piece of cake if we _____

5 Mr Bianci is in the yard

_____

6 The ship went on the rocks in the storm and _____

3 | *up* = TOWARDS, AS FAR AS
The small boy *ran up* to his mother and burst into tears.

come up   drive up   run up   walk up

Complete the paragraph, using a suitable phrasal verb from the list above.
Use each verb once only and put it in its correct form.

Ted Short is a trainee policeman. Yesterday was his first day on duty, and he

had to patrol the town all day. For several hours nothing at all happened.

Eventually, however, a young woman slowly ¹_____ _____ to him and

asked the way to the nearest hospital. A minute later a man

²_____ _____ and said he'd been robbed. At the same time a car

³_____ _____ , and the driver reported an accident. Ted was amazed.

Nothing had happened all day, and then three people had ⁴_____ _____

to him within a few minutes.

4 | *up* = FIRMLY, SECURELY
Why don't you *fasten up* the baby's coat? It's very cold today.

button sthg up   lock sthg up   tie sthg up   tighten sthg up

Rewrite the instructions, using a suitable verb. At (a) put the noun in brackets
between the verb and the particle and at (b) place it **after** the particle.

1 _____ up with string before you post it.   (the parcel)

(a) _____

(b) _____

2 Take a key so that you can _____ up before you leave.   (the equipment)

(a) _____

(b) _____

3 It's very wet. Why don't you _____ up?   (your raincoat)

(a) _____

(b) _____

4 _____ up before you put the plug back in the socket.   (the screws)

(a) _____

(b) _____

13 Revision (2)

1 Complete the newspaper reports, using suitable phrasal verbs (from units 7–12) with the same meaning as the word or phrase in brackets.

1
> Workmen ¹_____ (disconnected) the electricity in Tower Garden Flats to repair a fault yesterday. Unfortunately, they forgot to ²_____ (connect it) again after they had finished. As a result, several old people living on the upper floors thought the lift had ³_____ (stopped working) and phoned the caretaker up. Two people were inside the lift at the time and were unable to ⁴_____ (leave).

2
> Luke Short was ⁵_____ (allowed to go without being punished) this morning after the police had arrested him for lying about them. Judge Fair told Mr Short, however, never to ⁶_____ (invent) any more stories again about the behaviour of the police.

3
> The Red Wasps, the famous pop group, ⁷_____ (disappointed) their fans last night when they failed to ⁸_____ (appear) for the special concert they were due to give in Newton. One fan even climbed up on the stage and ⁹_____ (tore into small pieces) his ticket for their next concert.

4
> The price of oil last week ¹⁰_____ (rose) by 50%, ¹¹_____ (causing an increase in) air fares for all those about to go on holiday. Rutlanda, however, hopes to ¹²_____ (reduce) fares on its internal flights.

2 Each line of the paragraph below has a verb or particle missing. Draw a line (/) to show where the word should go and write the missing word in the blank on the right.

I up as soon as I heard someone knocking on the door.   1 _____

As soon as I opened it, two men rushed. One of the men put   2 _____

his hand in his pocket and out a small ring. 'That's Ben's,'   3 _____

I cried as I bent and looked at it. 'A strange old woman gave   4 _____

it to me,' he said. 'I don't believe you. You're making it,' I   5 _____

cried before running to pick the phone. I dialled and began   6 _____

to speak. But suddenly I was off. One of the men had put his   7 _____

hand on the phone while the other had a gun out and was   8 _____

pointing it at me.

3 Liana was very late for work yesterday. The pictures below show
you what happened to her before she arrived. Look at each picture
and tell the story. Use the phrasal verbs at the bottom of the
pictures. You must use the correct form and tense of each verb.
(For one picture you should use the verb in the passive.)

get up

hold up

come off

break down

dig up

slow down

_____

_____

_____

_____

_____

_____

_____

_____

_____

_____

_____

_____

⌊14⌋ *Away*, *off*, *out*

Look at the pictures below and write answers to the questions.

1

Why don't you apologise to Mr Talbot?
I can't. He's driven off.

4

What shall I do with the rest of the cake?
_____

2

Have you still got your parrot?
_____

5

What are they doing with the furniture?
_____

3

Where's your dog?
_____

6

Are Mr and Mrs Rosario in?
_____

2

out = EXTINGUISH, BE EXTINGUISHED
Please *put* your cigarette *out*. This is a no-smoking area.
The fire's *gone out*.

blow (a candle, etc.) out   go out   put (a fire, etc.) out

Complete the sentences, using a suitable verb from the list above.
Use each verb twice.

1 That fire's very dangerous. Can you help me to ___put___ it ___out___ ?

2 Two of the candles are still alight. Can you _____ them _____ ?

3 No smoking. Please _____ your cigarette _____ .

4 Put some more coal on the fire or it will _____ _____ .

5 There was a power cut and all the lights suddenly _____ _____ .

6 Make sure you _____ the match _____ after you've lit your pipe.

3

away/off/out = (MAKE) DISAPPEAR, (BE) GONE
Can you *clear* the cups *away*, please?
He *shaved* his beard *off*.
Can you *wash* this stain *out*?

clean (a house, room, etc.) out	get (a stain, mark, etc.) off/out
clean (a dirty mark, etc.) off	pour (water, etc.) away/out
clear sthg away	wipe (a stain, mark, etc.) off
empty sthg out	

Complete the conversation, using a suitable verb from the list above.
(Note that the particle is already given in each sentence.)

A: The students have left my flat in a terrible mess. I'll have to

   ¹ ___clear___ the place out!

B: Did they leave all this cigarette ash?

A: Yes. Just look at this ashtray. They didn't even ² _____ it out!

   They've even kept their bikes here. Look at that oil on the carpet!

B: How will you ³ _____ it out?

A: I've got no idea. And look at these dirty finger-marks on this wall!

   I'll never manage to ⁴ _____ them off.

B: They haven't even ⁵ _____ the dishes away after their last meal!

15 *Off*, *out*, *up*, *on*

1

off/out/up = COMPLETELY (DONE OR FINISHED)
I've *finished off* my work.
I need to *clear out* the study.
Eat everything *up*!

doze off	clear sthg out	dry (sthg) up
finish (sthg) off	cross sthg out	eat (sthg) up
kill sbdy off	rub sthg out	hurry up
	tire(d) out / be tired out	use sthg up

Complete the newspaper extracts, using a suitable phrasal verb from the list above.

1 — Goods worth almost one million dollars were stolen from Moxo Warehouse last night. Two guards employed by Moxo had _____ when the theft took place.

2 — There were reports that stocks of penicillin had been _____ in those areas where the fighting was at its worst.

3 — A mystery disease has _____ the sea-eagles in Newton City Zoo.

4 — It has been recently reported that there is now only a little water in the River Medan, and the upper part of the river has now _____. If the drought continues, water will soon be rationed.

5 — Six scouts have just completed a fifty-mile walk for charity and have now collected enough money to provide a holiday for hundred deprived children. The scouts were cheerful after their long walk but looked _____.

6 — Sharpley _____ the last year of his sporting career by breaking 5 world records.

Now match the headline with the extracts. Write the letter of the headline beside each article.

A **Exhausted but in good spirits**

B **Serious water shortage**

C **No medical supplies in war area**

D **A fitting end!**

E **Sweet dreams turn into nightmare**

F **Strange virus attacks rare birds**

2

on = CONTINUING
She *kept on* talking for over an hour.
The pupils *worked on* until the teacher returned.

sleep on (= continue sleeping)	work on (= continue working)
stay on (= stay longer)	carry on, go on, keep on (= continue)

give up (doing sthg) (= decide not to continue)
drop out (= stop attending or taking part in a course, leave your career)

Read the following short paragraph about Dave Lawson and answer the questions.

Last year Dave started to attend an optional training course but dropped out after a few weeks. Dave has a tendency to give up as soon as he meets a problem. He should keep on trying even when something is very difficult. Unfortunately, he never listens to advice and carries on doing whatever he wants without thinking of the consequences. In spite of these weaknesses, however, Dave is capable of doing well, and his teachers are now trying to persuade him to stay on at school so he can prepare for university.

1 What happened last year when Dave took a training course?

_____

2 What does Dave do when a problem arises?

_____

3 What advice would you give Dave?

_____

4 Do you think he will listen to your advice? Why (not)?

_____

5 What do Dave's teachers want him to do?

_____

3 Now write a few lines about someone who is exactly the opposite of Dave.

_____

_____

_____

_____

_____

16 *About, around, round, over*

1

about/around/round = HERE AND THERE, AIMLESSLY (often used to show a lack of purpose)

> Several pupils were *standing about* in the playground.
> I saw your pen *lying around* somewhere.
> Tom was *rushing round*, doing nothing really useful.

The particle *about* can usually be used instead of *around* and *round* with verbs like *standing, running, hurrying, lying,* etc.. However, we **cannot** use *about* instead of *around* and *round* with *look*.

> Would you like to come in and *look round*? (**not** *about*)

hurry about/around/round	stand about/around/round
kick (a ball) about/around	throw (a ball) about
lie about/around	wait about/around
look around/round	walk about/around/round
run about/around/round	wander about/around/round
rush about/around/round	

Complete the paragraph, describing the picture with a suitable verb from the list above.

A few small boys are laughing and ¹ running about on

the beach while a tall man is ²_____ _____ . He is

carrying a chair but he doesn't know where to put it. Two women

are ³_____ _____ , looking bored while three young

men are ⁴_____ _____ on the sand. Three girls are

⁵_____ a small ball _____ , and a little boy is

⁶_____ a large ball _____ .

2

| round = TO EVERYBODY IN A GROUP, etc. |
| Can you *pass* the sweets *round*, please? |

| hand sthg round | pass sthg round | offer sthg round | take sthg round |

Write a sentence to describe each picture, using one of the phrasal verbs above.

1    3

1 She <u>is offering some chocolate round.</u>

2 She _____

2    4

3 They _____

4 He _____

3

| Come *round* to see us tonight. |
| Come *over* here a moment, please. |
| (*round/over* = MOVEMENT OVER A SHORT DISTANCE) |
| **Note** |
| *bring someone round* can also mean 'help someone who has fainted to regain consciousness'. |

| wander round | cycle round | hurry round |
| come round | drive round/over | bring sthg/someone round |

Answer the questions below, using a suitable phrasal verb from the list above.
(Do not use the verb *come*.)

1 Can you come and show me your new car?
   I'll drive round now if you like.

2 Can you come over some time? You can leave your bicycle in the entrance.

   _____

3 Can you come over as fast as you can? It's quite urgent.

   _____

4 Can you come over any time you're free? It isn't far to walk.

   _____

5 Can you come over, and get Ted and Dave to accompany you?

   _____

17 *Down, off*

<table>
<tr><td>1</td><td>down</td><td>=</td><td>GENERALLY CONCERNED WITH FAILURE, DESTRUCTION, DAMAGE, HARM, ETC. AND BEING IN A WORSE CONDITION</td></tr>
<tr><td></td><td>off</td><td>=</td><td>GENERALLY CONCERNED WITH SUCCESS, ETC. AND BEING IN A BETTER CONDITION</td></tr>
</table>

break down	The engine's stopped. I wonder why it's *broken down*.
	When she heard the sad news, she *broke down* and wept.
come/go down with (an illness)	A lot of my friends have *come / gone down with* flu.
let sbdy down	You *let* us all *down* when you didn't come to the meeting.
pull sthg down	I hope they don't *pull* this lovely old building *down*.
put sbdy down	Tom's always *putting* me *down*: I think he's jealous of me.
turn sthg down	Think carefully about my offer before you *turn it down*.
turn sbdy down	Ted proposed to Rosie but she *turned* him *down*.
bring/pull sthg off	The trick looked impossible but Ken *pulled* it *off*.
come off	It was a good attempt, but it didn't quite *come off*.
hit it off	Sue *hit* it *off* with Ann and they soon became close friends.
pay off	All your hard work has at last *paid off*. You've passed!
show (sthg) off	Stop boasting and *showing off*. Be more modest.

Complete the sentences, using phrasal verbs from the list above and any other necessary words.

1 You can rely on me: I won't _let you down_____ .

2 It may be difficult to persuade the government to recommend our company's products, but I'm sure the new sales manager will _____ .

3 Don't worry about Ann and her new colleagues. She's a very friendly person, and I know she'll _____ .

4 All the time you spend practising will be very useful. You'll find it will

   _____ .

5 In one way it was a good idea to perform the play about Ancient Greece with actors wearing modern dress, but nevertheless I felt that something was strange about it. It didn't quite _____ .

6 Stop criticising Thomas and saying unkind things about him. I don't know why you enjoy

   _____ .

7 I hadn't the qualifications for the job, and so they _____ .

8 Don't try to be so clever? No one likes people who are always _____ .

2 Complete the newspaper extracts, using a suitable phrasal verb from the list in exercise 1.

1 —— The city council plans to _____ the old city hall in order to make room for a large supermarket. The city hall has been an attractive landmark for over a hundred years.

2 —— Months of intensive practice, long training sessions and careful planning _____ yesterday as Skudai United defeated Tusukuba Rovers 5–2 in the Finals of the White Rose League.

3 —— The President's car yesterday _____ as he was touring Lasida. He was in the middle of the prohibited area in the north of the state when it suddenly came to a halt.

4 —— Fibre Optics Limited yesterday _____ a fifty-million-dollar deal. They won the contract to supply lenses to cameras to be fitted on board all rockets in the government's future space programme.

5 —— Len Big's attempt to become world heavyweight champion by winning his first fight against Rory Randall almost _____ last night. Big knocked his opponent down in the first round but failed to take advantage of his good fortune.

6 —— Requests by ten refugees to stay in Lavia were _____ by the government. The refugees will be sent back to Rurandia in ten days unless they appeal to the President.

Now match the headlines with the extracts. Write the letter of the headline beside each article.

A **Immigration permits refused**

B **No-go area**

C **Historic building to disappear**

D **Boxer almost succeeds in gaining crown**

E **Manufacturer looks forward with confidence**

F **Team's hard work rewarded**

3 Complete the joke, using a phrasal verb from the list in exercise 1.

'What did people say to the man who managed to escape from a straitjacket?'

'You've _____ it _____ .'

18 *Out, to*

1

out = LOSING CONSCIOUSNESS	*to* = REGAINING CONSCIOUSNESS

black out	I couldn't remember a thing after falling. I just *blacked out*.
pass out	Poor Mary Lee *passed out* when she saw all the blood.
knock out	Big Jim Jones struck his opponent and *knocked* him *out*.
come to	Suddenly I felt a blow on the head and everything went black. When I *came to*, I found myself in a small room. (**Note** *come round* is also used with this meaning, particularly after an operation.)

Answer the questions below, using a phrasal verb from the list above.

1 What does a boxer try to do by hitting his opponent hard on the chin?

    _____

2 What might happen if you fall and bang your head hard on the pavement?

    _____

3 What do nurses usually make sure a patient does as soon as possible

   after an operation?

    _____

2

out = GENERALLY CONCERNED WITH SOLUTIONS TO DIFFICULTIES, ETC.	

sort sthg out	We had a quarrel, but we've sorted everything out now and we're good friends again.
iron sthg out	Did you manage to iron out all the difficulties?
have sthg out	Tell me exactly why you don't trust us. Let's have it out so that we can put an end to this unpleasantness.
turn out	At first there were problems but it turned out all right.

Complete the conversation, using a phrasal verb from the list above.
Use each verb once.

B: I think the company's got quite a few problems to ¹_____ _____ .

A: But they don't seem interested at all in their customers. I'm going to see the

    manager and ²_____ it _____ with him.

B: I agree. They certainly need someone to ³_____ them _____ .

A: No doubt things will ⁴_____ _____ all right eventually but they must

    provide more help for their customers in the meantime.

19 *Up* (2)

<table>
<tr><td>**1**</td><td colspan="2">*up* = GENERALLY CONCERNED WITH IMAGINING AND INVENTING</td></tr>
<tr><td></td><td>dream sthg up
(often scornful)</td><td>I wonder who *dreamt up* such a silly rule?</td></tr>
<tr><td></td><td>make sthg up
(excuses & stories)</td><td>Stop *making up* excuses and tell us the real reason why you were late.</td></tr>
<tr><td></td><td>think sthg up</td><td>What an amazing machine! I wonder what its inventor will *think up* next.</td></tr>
</table>

Miscellaneous	
blow sthg up	There's no bridge now: the rebels have *blown* it *up*.
crop up	I'll see you at the same time next Monday unless something *crops up* at the last minute.
hold sbdy up	Two masked men with guns *held up* the people in the bank.
look up	Business is *looking up* and we're making a profit at last.
pick sbdy/sthg up	I'll *pick* you *up* at eight: you'll like riding in my new car.
put sbdy up	I'm sure Mrs Sims can *put* you *up* for the night.

Complete the sentences, using a phrasal verb from the lists above.

1 (*in an office*) 'Business is <u>looking</u> <u>up</u> . Look at the

   huge profit we've just made.'

2 (*at a meeting*) 'Sorry, I'm late. Something _____ _____

   and I had to deal with it before I could come.'

3 (*one soldier to another*) 'The enemy have just

   _____ _____ the bridge. We'll have to swim across the

   river!'

4 (*on a stormy night*) 'Our car has broken down. Can you

   _____ us _____ for the night?'

5 (*about a person at work*) 'I don't have a car, and Mr Byland

   _____ me _____ on his way to the office every morning.'

6 (*in a cowboy film*) 'Some robbers have _____ _____ the

   train and are taking the gold.'

7 (*about a strange invention*) 'Who on earth _____ _____

   such a strange device? What does it do?'

8 (*in a quarrel*) 'I don't believe you've ever flown a plane.

   You're _____ it _____ .'

20 Three-word phrasal verbs

The following phrasal verbs consist of three words: verb + adverb + preposition.
Both noun and pronoun objects follow the preposition. Almost all three-word
phrasal verbs follow this pattern:

'I'm not going to *put up with such rude behaviour.*'
'I'm not going to *put up with it*, either.'

boil down to sthg	I don't know which job you ought to take. I suppose it *boils down to* whether you want a desk job or a job outdoors.
catch up with sbdy	Carry on walking. I'll run and *catch up with* you.
come in for (blame, etc.)	The government's new plan *came in for* a lot of criticism.
do away with sthg	Most countries *did away with* slavery long ago.
face up to sthg	Mrs Azumo must *face up to* it: she'll never fully recover.
get away with sthg	You always forget to do your homework, but you're never punished. How do you *get away with* it?
get down to (work)	I must *get down to* work now: the exams start next week.
get on (well) with sbdy	Ben didn't *get on with* Tim: they were always quarrelling.
get round to sthg	I intended to write but I never *got round to* it. I had no time.
go back on (a promise)	You must come. Don't *go back on* your word. You promised!
go in for sthg	Are you *going in for* this competition?
look forward to sthg	We're all *looking forward to* seeing you again next week.
make away/off with sthg	The robbers *made away with* all Mrs Lee's jewellery.
put up with sbdy/sthg	How does Linda *put up with* such a selfish husband?

1 Complete sentence (b) of each pair below so that it is similar in meaning
to sentence (a). Use a suitable phrasal verb from the list above.

1 (a) Such behaviour shouldn't be tolerated.

   (b) No one should have to put up with such behaviour.

2 (a) Don't ignore the problem.

   (b) You must _____

3 (a) Tom and I were always good friends.

   (b) I always _____

4 (a) Why have you never been punished for being late every morning?

   (b) How have you _____

5 (a) It is a complicated problem but the important thing about it
     is a demand for higher wages.

   (b) It is a complicated problem but it all _____

6 (a) I must start revising or else I shall fail the exams.

   (b) I shall fail the exams if I don't _____

7 (a) Keep to the promise you made to the children.

   (b) Don't _____

8 (a) The death penalty has been abolished by many countries.

   (b) Many countries _____

2 Look at the situations in the pictures. Complete the sentences,
using a suitable phrasal verb from the list at the beginning of this unit.

1

The hotel has *come in for a lot of* _____
criticism.

4

The school has _____

_____ uniforms.

2

Perhaps Mr Brown will _____

cutting the grass one of these days.

5

Mary _____

_____ a lot of competitions.

3

So much traffic! I'm really _____

_____ getting home.

6

A burglar _____

_____ the TV set.

21 People

ask sbdy round	Why don't you *ask* Ted *round* for a meal this evening?
come round	I don't want to go out. Ann's *coming round* this evening.
drop in	Please *drop in* any time. I'm always happy to see you.
get on (well) (with sbdy)	Dave *got on* well *with* Ken, and they became good friends.
go out	'Would you like to *go out* tonight?' Ali asked his wife.
go round	Ken decided to *go round* to see how his neighbour was.
look forward to sthg/ doing sthg	I'm *looking forward to* seeing my old school friends again.
meet up (with sbdy)	Let's *meet up* after the concert and have something to eat.
pick sbdy/sthg up	I'll *pick* Ben *up*: his flat is on the way to the sports ground.
put sbdy up	Stay here. We can *put* you *up* in our spare room.
run/bump into sbdy	Guess who I *ran into* today! Beluti Sadri! What a surprise!
stay in	I'm *staying in* tonight. I don't feel like going out.
stay out	Don't *stay out* too late. Try to come home before ten.
take sbdy out	My uncle Victor is *taking* us *out* for a meal this evening.

1 Complete the paragraph below, using phrasal verbs which mean the same as the words in brackets. Add pronouns if necessary.

Who do you think ¹_____*dropped in*_____ (called at

my house) last night? It was Henry. He called because he

wanted to ²_____ (invite me to go

with him) for a meal. I had ³_____

(met him by chance) in the post office the previous day. He told

me then that he was ⁴_____

(anticipating with pleasure) the chance of having a chat with me.

When he called to see me last night, he arranged to

⁵_____ (come and

collect me in his car) at seven o'clock on Friday.

We have always ⁶_____

(been very friendly), and I'm sure we'll have a

very enjoyable time together.

2 Fill in the blanks in the questionnaire below with a suitable particle.

HOW FRIENDLY ARE YOU?

1 Which of the following do you get _on_ _with_ best of all?
   A Other people ❑   **B** Animals ❑   **C** Children ❑

2 Do you prefer to go _____
   A with only one close friend? ❑   **B** with a lot of friends? ❑   **C** by yourself? ❑

3 If you ran _____ an old friend, would you
   A talk about old times? ❑   **B** say hello and walk on? ❑
   C arrange to meet _____ soon? ❑

4 Which of the following do you prefer to do in the evenings?
   A Stay _____ and watch TV ❑   **B** Go _____ with a friend ❑
   C Ask a friend _____ ❑

5 A friend without a car visits you and will probably stay very late. Would you
   A offer to put your friend _____ for the night? ❑
   B advise your friend not to stay _____ too late and go back home early? ❑
   C wait and later call a taxi to take your friend home? ❑

6 When someone you don't like too much phones and asks if they can
   come _____ to see you, would you
   A say you were looking _____ _____ seeing them? ❑
   B ask them to come _____ some time later? ❑
   C make excuses and say you were going _____? ❑

7 If some new neighbours came to live next door to you, would you
   A go _____ to welcome them after a few days? ❑
   B just say hello if you happened to see them? ❑
   C invite them at once to drop _____ to see you? ❑

8 In the evening, do you prefer to go _____ to:
   A a cinema? ❑   **B** a party? ❑   **C** a shopping centre?

Now answer the questions to find out how friendly you are. Then
check your answers, using the scores below.

1 **A** 3	**B** 1	**C** 2	18 – 24 points	=	You are very sociable and friendly. You love
2 **A** 2	**B** 3	**C** 1			doing things with other people.
3 **A** 2	**B** 1	**C** 3	12 – 17 points	=	You are friendly but you can also enjoy
4 **A** 1	**B** 2	**C** 3			being on your own.
5 **A** 3	**B** 1	**C** 2	Below 12 points	=	You ought to try to get on better with other
6 **A** 3	**B** 2	**C** 1			people. Are you really an unfriendly person?
7 **A** 2	**B** 1	**C** 3			
8 **A** 1	**B** 3	**C** 2			

22 Food

boil over	Turn the heat down, please. The water's *boiling over*.
chop up	Those are too big. *Chop* the meat *up* into smaller pieces.
cut down on sthg	*Cut down on* fried food if you want to lose weight.
cut sthg out	The doctor advised Henry to *cut* all eggs *out* of his diet.
dig in (slang)	Here's the meal. I know you're very hungry, so *dig in*.
dish (food) out	Will you help me to *dish* the rice *out* to all our guests?
dish (food) up	The meal's ready now. Shall I *dish* it *up*?
eat in	Let's stay at home and *eat in* tonight. I don't want to go out.
eat out	Let's *eat out* tonight. Do you know any good restaurants?
get through (food, etc.)	Do you think we can *get through* all this food?
rustle (a meal, etc.) up	She always manages to *rustle up* something to eat.
serve up	Is everyone ready to eat? Can I *serve* the food *up* now?
tuck in (informal)	'*Tuck in*, boys,' he said when the meal was ready.
tuck into (food, etc.)	Sue sat down, smiled and at once *tucked into* her dinner.
wolf (food) down	You should eat slowly. You always *wolf* everything *down*.

1 Complete the paragraph, using a suitable phrasal verb from the list below.

chop up	boil over	put in	tuck in
drop in	jump up	rustle up	dish out
pour in	cut up	sit down	take out

When I ¹_dropped in___ to see Joe, he asked me to stay for a meal. 'I'll soon ²_____ something _____ for us,' he said. I was about to sit down when he said, 'Before you sit down, could you ³_____ _____ a saucepan and ⁴_____ _____ about two litres of water?' After he had put the water on the cooker, he ⁵_____ _____ and began to tell me about all the dishes he could make. Suddenly he ⁶_____ _____ and ran to the cooker. 'Oh dear!' he cried. 'You've let the water ⁷_____ _____!' The next moment he turned to me again. 'Can you see a packet of hot sour mix?' he asked. I pointed to a small packet under his nose. He took the lid off the saucepan, ⁸_____ _____ the hot sour mix and began to stir vigorously. 'If you ⁹_____ _____ some small pieces of chicken, I can add them to the soup,' he said, handing me a knife. After the soup had been cooking for twenty minutes or so, Joe then asked me to wash some lettuce and ¹⁰_____ it _____ . 'Now ¹¹_____ _____ the soup in those small bowls and serve it with the chopped lettuce,' he told me. 'Then ¹²_____ _____ and enjoy the soup I've made!'

2 You have a friend who is becoming overweight. What advice would you give them about food and eating? (Use a phrasal verb containing *cut* in your answer.)

_____

_____

3 Complete the conversation, using phrasal verbs from the list at the beginning of this unit. Use a different verb in each gap.

A: Shall we ¹__*eat*__ __*out*__ tonight?

B: No, let's ²_____ ____ . I just feel like staying at home.

A: But have we got enough food for a meal?

B: Yes, I can soon ³_____ ____ something you like. Why don't you watch TV while I do the cooking?

(*30 minutes later*)

B: It's ready. Shall I ⁴_____ it ____ now?

A: Yes, please. This programme's almost over.

B: Good. Here it is, so ⁵_____ ____ . It's chicken – your favourite.

A: You've given me too many potatoes. I don't think I can ⁶____ _____ them all. Take some off my plate and have them yourself.

B: No, thanks. I'm trying to ⁷_____ ____ ____ potatoes. I've got to lose weight. Anyway, I'm sure you can eat it all. You usually ⁸_____ ____ everything on your plate.

A: Yes, but it's different tonight. I ate some chocolates while you were cooking!

23 Health

ask after sbdy	Joe was *asking after* you: I said you were better now.
black/pass out	I fell and *blacked out*: I can't remember anything.
break out in (spots, etc.)	Poor Anna has *broken out in* a cold sweat.
come down with (an illness)	I've *come down with* flu, and so I can't see you today.
come round	My head ached when I *came round* after the accident.
come out in (spots, etc.)	Don't go near Pete: he's just *come out in* spots.
drop off	The old man *dropped off* (fell asleep) while watching television.
ease off	My toothache *eased off* after I'd taken two tablets.
get over (an illness, etc.)	Sue's *got over* her recent illness and is back at work.
go down with (an illness)	A lot of pupils have *gone down with* measles.
let up	My toothache is very bad: the pain won't *let up*.
pass away (= die)	Poor old Harry's *passed away*: we'll all miss him.
throw up	The baby tried to eat a biscuit and *threw up* (vomited).
wear off	Take a tablet, and the pain will soon *wear off*.
(have/go for) a check-up	All the pupils are going to the school nurse for *a check-up* today.
(be/feel) run down	I just feel tired every day: I think I'm *run down*.

1 Read the conversation below. Who do you think is speaking and where is the conversation taking place? Now complete it by writing a particle in each gap. (All the phrasal verbs about health are included in the list above but there are also some general phrasal verbs.)

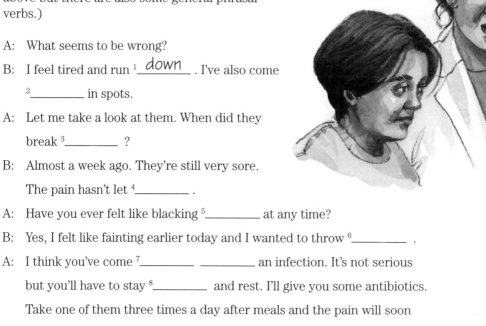

A: What seems to be wrong?

B: I feel tired and run ¹ _down_ . I've also come

²_____ in spots.

A: Let me take a look at them. When did they

break ³_____ ?

B: Almost a week ago. They're still very sore.

The pain hasn't let ⁴_____ .

A: Have you ever felt like blacking ⁵_____ at any time?

B: Yes, I felt like fainting earlier today and I wanted to throw ⁶_____ .

A: I think you've come ⁷_____ _____ an infection. It's not serious

but you'll have to stay ⁸_____ and rest. I'll give you some antibiotics.

Take one of them three times a day after meals and the pain will soon

ease ⁹_____ . Carry ¹⁰_____ taking the antibiotics for a week and

then see me again. If you begin to feel worse, please phone me at once.

2 Give suitable advice to someone who:

1 has broken out in a cold sweat.

_____

2 has just come round after blacking out.

_____

3 has gone down with a bad cold.

_____

4 wants to be sure they're all right.

_____

3 Read the doctor's advice to a patient below. Write brief directions suitable for putting on the bottle of medicine about which he/she is talking. Avoid using phrasal verbs where possible and do not use short forms (e.g. _you've_). You may need a dictionary.

'Take this medicine if you frequently break out in cold sweats. You can also take it if ever you feel like throwing up or passing out. Avoid driving or using machinery after you've taken the medicine in case you suddenly drop off. If you've got a headache or stomachache, you can take the medicine until the pain wears off. If the pain doesn't let up or if you continue to feel like throwing up, however, you should see a doctor as soon as possible. This medicine is not intended for people who feel run down or who are getting over a serious illness.'

_____

_____

_____

_____

_____

_____

_____

_____

_____

_____

_____

_____

Travelling

break down	The bus has *broken down*. We have to get out and walk.
drive off/away	Ann *drove off* after the accident without telling the police.
drive on	Don't stop here. *Drive on* to the next garage.
fill (a petrol tank) up	I've got very little petrol left. I'd better *fill up* at the next garage.
go through (traffic lights)	Look at that car. It *went through* the red lights.
knock sbdy/sthg down	The bus has just *knocked* poor Danny *down*.
pull in/over	The police signalled to me to *pull in/over* and stop at the side of the busy road.
pull out	Dave suddenly *pulled out* into the middle of the road.
pull up	I'll *pull up* here so you can get out of the car.
slow down	You're going too fast. *Slow down*!
speed up	We're crawling. Can you *speed up* a little or I'll be late?

1 Fill in the blanks in the questionnaire below. (Note that most of the phrasal verbs used are concerned with travelling and are in the list above, but a few other common phrasal verbs are also used.)

1 The car you are travelling in breaks _down_ . Do you
  a get _____ and walk? ❑   *b* try to repair it? ❑   *c* ring _____ the nearest garage? ❑

2 It is dark, and you have just got into your car. What is the first thing you do?
  a Start the engine. ❑   *b* Turn the headlights _____ ❑   *c* Fasten your seat belt. ❑

3 You accidentally knock someone _____ , but you don't think the person is badly injured. Do you
  a slow _____ to see they are all right and then drive _____ ? ❑
  b pull _____ , give them first aid and then go the nearest telephone? ❑
  c pick the person _____ and drive _____ to the nearest hospital? ❑

4 You get in your car and you are about to leave. Do you first
  a look in your rear mirror to make sure there are no cars behind? ❑
  b put your hand _____ and pull _____ into the middle of the road? ❑
  c switch _____ your indicator and then drive _____ slowly? ❑

5 You have some petrol but not a lot, and you see a petrol station. Do you
  a drive _____ and try to get to your destination? ❑
  b slow _____ and look out for the next petrol station? ❑
  c pull _____ and fill _____ ? ❑

6 The lights are changing from green to amber. Do you
  a pull _____ ❑
  b speed _____ and go straight _____ them? ❑
  C slow _____ a little but drive _____ ? ❑

Now answer the questions to find out how good a driver you are.
Then check your answers using the scores below.

1	**A** 1	**B** 3	**C** 2	16 – 18 points	=	You are probably a very good driver.
2	**A** 2	**B** 1	**C** 3	12 – 15 points	=	You are an average driver.
3	**A** 1	**B** 3	**C** 2	Below 12 points	=	Don't go near a car!
4	**A** 3	**B** 1	**C** 2			
5	**A** 1	**B** 2	**C** 3			
6	**A** 3	**B** 1	**C** 2			

2

check (sthg) in	Let's *check* our luggage *in* first and then have a coffee.
see sbdy off	All Anna's friends went to the station to *see* her *off*.
set off	Let's *set off* early and then we can arrive before lunch.
take off	The plane *took off* a few minutes after we'd got on.
hold sbdy/sthg up (often passive)	Our flight was *held up* by the airport workers' strike.

Complete the conversation, using a suitable phrasal verb which means the same as the verb or phrase in italics.

A: What time did you ¹ _set off_ from home this morning?

B: We *left* at half past six.

A: How long did it take you to get to the airport?

B: Only half an hour. We reached the airport at seven.

A: Did you ² _____ _____ as soon as you arrived?

B: Yes, we *handed in our tickets and gave in our luggage* then.

A: Did anyone go with you to ³ _____ you _____?

B: Yes, my brother *came with us to say goodbye*.

A: What time did your plane ⁴ _____ _____ ?

B: It didn't *leave* until half past nine, so we had plenty of time to talk.

A: But I thought it should have left at ten past eight. Why was it ⁵ _____ _____ ?

B: It was the fog that *delayed* us. We were very lucky to be able to leave.

Telephoning

be through	(Operator) Go ahead and speak. You're *through* now.
call sbdy up	Katie's going to *call* you *up* tonight.
cut sbdy off (often passive)	We were in the middle of an interesting conversation when we were *cut off*.
get through (to sbdy)	'Did you *get through* to Ken?' 'Yes, I spoke to him at last.'
hang up	I *hung up* when Ben began to insult me.
hold on	The operator asked me to *hold on* while she connected us.
look sthg up	Can you *look up* Mary's number in the phone directory?
phone sbdy up	Please *phone* us *up* as soon as you get home.
put the phone/ the receiver down	'Why did you *put* the receiver *down* so quickly?' 'The person at the other end of the line was very rude to me.'
put sbdy through	I asked the receptionist to *put* me *through* to the manager.
ring sbdy back	Can you ask Sue to *ring* me *back* when she returns?
ring off	The caller *rang off* before I could ask for her number.
ring sbdy up	Linda promised to *ring* the theatre *up* and book two seats.

1 Complete the conversation, using phrasal verbs from the list above.

A: Do you know the number of Lawson Mount Hospital?

B: I'm sorry, I don't. Why don't you ¹__look__ it __up__ in the directory?

A: I don't have a directory for that area.

B: Well, ²_____ _____ directory enquiries.

A: Oh, here's the number. It's 774492. I'd written it on this bit of paper. Hello, is that Lawson Mount Hospital? Can you ³_____ me _____ to Ward 2, please?

C: ⁴_____ _____ a moment, please.

A: Hello, is that Ward 2? Can I speak to . . .? That's strange. The line's gone dead. We've been ⁵_____ _____ .

B: ⁶_____ the phone _____ , wait a moment and then dial the number again. I'm sure you'll eventually ⁷_____ _____ to the hospital.

A: All right. Here goes! (*pause*) Hello, is that Ward 2? I'd . . . . Would you believe it? They've ⁸_____ _____ !

B: They can't have done that. There's obviously something wrong with the phone.

2 What do you think the people in the pictures are saying? Match the sentences with the pictures.

A   You're through now.

B   I think we've been cut off.

C   I'll have to hang up now.

D   That's the last time I'll ask to be put through to the manager.

3 Read the telephone conversation below. Substitute expressions containing a phrasal verb for the words and expressions in italics.

CALLER: Can I speak to Sue Brown, please?

OPERATOR: Just a moment, please. I'll [1] *connect you.*

(after a few seconds)

OPERATOR: Go ahead, caller, You [2] *are connected* now.

SECRETARY: Sue Brown's office.

CALLER: Hello. Is Sue Brown there, please?

SECRETARY: No, I'm afraid she's just gone out. Would you like to leave a message?

CALLER: Well, tell her I [3] *phoned her.* Actually, I've been trying to [4] *reach her by telephone* for a couple of days. Tell her that the last time I phoned, the operator [5] *stopped our conversation* before we'd finished. I don't want her to think that I [6] *finished the conversation by replacing the receiver.* In fact, I [7] *waited* for ten minutes, but the line was completely dead. Could you ask her to [8] *return my telephone call* this evening?

1 _____

2 _____

3 _____

4 _____

5 _____

6 _____

7 _____

8 _____

26 Police and crime

break in/break into sthg	Burglars *broke in* while we were out and stole $1000.
break out/break out of sthg	Six prisoners managed to *break out* and run off.
bump sbdy off (slang)	Who do the police think *bumped* Mr Big *off*?
catch sbdy out	The police *caught* him *out* when he said he was at the cinema: it was closed at the time.
do away with sbdy (slang)	Someone's *done away with* him: he's been shot.
do sbdy in (slang)	Ted couldn't have *done* him *in*. He didn't have a gun.
do sbdy out of sthg	Katie was *done out of* $20 by the dishonest salesman.
get away with (a crime, etc.)	'You'll never *get away with* it,' Tom told the kidnapper.
get off with (a warning, etc.)	He's lucky to *get off with* a warning and not be fined.
give oneself up	The criminals *gave* themselves *up* to the police.
go for sbdy	I was so angry that I *went for* the burglars with a stick.
hold sbdy up	The gang took out their guns and *held* us *up*.
let sbdy off	The judge *let* Mary *off* as no one had proved her guilty.
look into sthg	The police are *looking into* the case of the missing ring.
make off with sthg	The thieves opened the safe and *made off with* $1000.

1 Read the sentences below. Inspector Sharp is talking to a newspaper reporter.

Inspector Sharp

Someone has murdered Mr Sims.
We have no definite knowledge of who killed him.
However, Mr Sims cheated Bill Low out of a large amount of money.
If it's Bill Low, we don't expect he'll surrender to the authorities without a fight.
He attacked a policeman once.
He even escaped with the policeman's gun.

Now read the following sentences. Big Joe, a well-known criminal, is talking to one of his friends. Although Big Joe gives the same information as the inspector, he uses slang and colloquial English. Complete the longer blanks with appropriate verbs and the shorter blanks with particles.

Big Joe

Someone's ¹_____ Mr Sims _____ .

I've got no idea who ²_____ him _____ .

But old Sims ³_____ Bill Low _____ _____ a lot of money.

If it's Bill, he won't ⁴_____ himself _____ without a fight.

He ⁵_____ _____ a policeman once.

He even ⁶_____ _____ _____ the policeman's gun.

54

2 What do you think is happening in each picture? Write sentences, using a phrasal verb from the list below.

break in   hold up   break out   make off with

1 _____

2 _____

3 _____

4 _____

3 Complete the newspaper extracts, using a suitable phrasal verb from the list at the beginning of this unit. (Use different phrasal verbs for the two blanks in no. 3.)

1 —
> Inspector Clue has now been appointed to _____ the recent hold-up at the Bank of India. He is talking to all the staff.

2 —
> The girlfriend of a bank robber suddenly _____ an off-duty policeman who was out shopping with his family. Onlookers said the girl was carrying a knife and tried to stab the policeman.

3 —
> A youth who threatened a schoolgirl and two small boys was _____ with a warning when he appeared in court today. The judge said that the youth would not _____ so lightly if he appeared in court again. The next time he would be sent to prison.

4 —
> Thieves _____ the home of Dr and Mrs William Lee last night and _____ several diamond rings and bracelets.

Now match the headlines with the extracts. Write the letter of the headline in the space by each article.

A **Jewellery stolen**

B **Woman attacks policeman**

C **Famous detective to investigate robbery**

D **Bully given warning**

27 Feelings

break down	When he heard the sad news, he *broke down* and wept.
browned off (passive) (slang)	Katie soon got *browned off* with waiting and left.
(not) care for sbdy/sthg	I don't *care for* people who are unreliable.
carry away (usually passive)	I got *carried away* when I was arguing and completely forgot about the time.
cheer (sbdy) up	I hope this good news *cheers* you *up. Cheer up!*
cut up (usually passive)	We were very *cut up* when we heard about the accident.
fall for sbdy	Tom's *fallen for* Anna and can't take his eyes off her!
fall out with sbdy	Ben *fell out with* Annie and stopped speaking to her.
fed up (with sbdy/sthg) (passive)	I'm *fed up* with listening to all your complaints.
flare up	Maria *flared up* when she heard Simon insult her friend.
get on/along (well) (with sbdy)	I always *got along* with Sarah: we never quarrelled.
let sbdy down	You *let* me *down.* I waited an hour but you never came.
pick on sbdy	Why *pick on* Ben? He wasn't the only boy to be late.
put sbdy/sthg down	I didn't like to hear you *putting* everyone *down.* Why can't you say something good about people?
strike up a friendship	We *struck up* a friendship as soon as we met.
take sbdy aback (often passive)	I was *taken aback* by Mr Talbot's refusal to let me have half a day off work to attend my brother's wedding.
take to sbdy	I *took to* Sue at once and we soon became good friends.
warm to/towards sbdy	Many people *warmed to* Mr Lee when he spoke about the hardships he had overcome.

1 Read each of the following sentences about the different ways six people felt.
Then complete the sentences, using a suitable phrasal verb.

1 Anna felt sad and miserable.
2 Ben was shocked.
3 Pete suddenly felt extremely angry.
4 Joe felt disappointed.
5 Sue was bored.
6 Katie began to feel happier than previously.

PETE: Anger [1]_____ inside me when Ann told me what Ben had said.

SUE: I'm [2]_____ . I've been washing and drying dishes all day long.

BEN: I was quite [3]_____ – it wasn't like him to be so rude.

KATIE: I certainly [4]_____ when I heard the good news.

ANNA: I just felt like [5]_____ and bursting into tears.

JOE: You can imagine how [6]_____ I felt when Ron didn't turn up.

2 Rewrite the story below, replacing the words in italics with the most suitable phrasal verbs from the list at the beginning of this unit.

Simon and I used to [1] *be very friendly* with each other, but then Simon [2] *quarrelled with* Sarah. Simon had never [3] *liked* Sarah, and he started to [4] *criticise* her whenever he was with me. Eventually Simon and I quarrelled, too. Some time later, however, Simon slowly [5] *began to like* Sarah and she also began to [6] *feel a liking for* him. They soon [7] *formed* a close friendship, and Sarah stopped seeing me. I now feel very [8] *upset* about the whole matter.

_____

_____

_____

_____

_____

_____

_____

_____

_____

_____

3 Give suitable advice to someone who

1 often flares up when someone upsets them.

_____

2 always needs cheering up when you see them.

_____

3 is fed up doing their present job.

_____

4 easily gets carried away when they watch a football match.

_____

5 is badly cut up after a quarrel with a friend.

_____

28 Revision (3)

1

Read the statements below and write questions, using the name and verb given in brackets.

1 Rosie is on friendly terms with Anna. (Helen – get)
   Does Helen get on with Anna, too?

2 Tom can provide one of the students with accommodation.

   (Miss Tay – put)

   _____

3 Bill Blunt surrendered to the police. (Harry Smart – give)

   _____

4 Sam put the phone down when he heard Sue's voice. (Ken – hang)

   _____

5 Linda's train was delayed for over an hour. (Rikako's train – hold)

   _____

6 Angelica met Spiros accidentally in the supermarket. (Hassan – run)

   _____

2

Complete the paragraph. From the list below, use a suitable phrasal verb which means the same as the word or words in brackets. Note that the word *check-up* is a noun formed from a phrasal verb.

black out	check-up	come down with	come to
cut out	face up to	go up	run down

I had been feeling [1]_____ (tired and unwell) for several weeks but yesterday at work I

suddenly felt sick and [2]_____ (lost consciousness). A nurse was standing over me

when I eventually [3]_____ (regained consciousness). I told her that I had high blood

pressure, and she advised me to have a [4]_____ (medical examination) as soon as

possible. Later that day, after examining me, my doctor said that my blood pressure had

[5]_____ (increased) and was now dangerously high. He changed the pills I was taking

and then ordered me to have a complete rest for a few days and [6]_____ (stop) all

violent forms of exercise. He thought that I had also probably [7]_____ (caught) a nasty

viral infection. He said that I must [8]_____ (learn to accept) the fact that I had high

blood pressure and stop rushing around so much.

3 What happened to Harry? Write sentences using the phrasal verbs in the boxes.

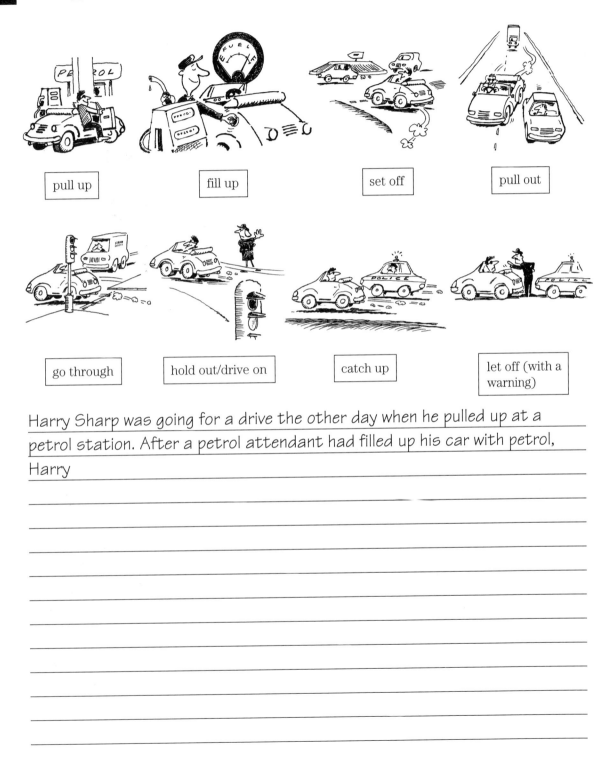

pull up   fill up   set off   pull out

go through   hold out/drive on   catch up   let off (with a warning)

Harry Sharp was going for a drive the other day when he pulled up at a
petrol station. After a petrol attendant had filled up his car with petrol,
Harry

Answer key

Introduction

4 *The following verbs should be circled:*
pick up   throw away   cleared up   found out   came back   going away   run off   taken out   threw away

5 1 got on 2 got up 3 turned up 4 found out 5 set off 6 pulled up 7 (were) worn out 8 got back

[1] Recognising phrasal verbs 1

1 1 going past 2 turning round 3 coming back 4 getting out 5 coming over

2 1 get in 2 woke up 3 shouted out 4 get out 5 got up 6 ran off 7 come back

3 1 Why is the bus going past without stopping?
2 Why is the balloon coming/falling down?
3 Why is the bird flying away?
4 Why is the man turning round?
5 Why is the woman looking up?

[2] Recognising phrasal verbs 2

1 1 hold out 2 holding down 3 held up 4 Hold on 5 holding back 6 hold over 7 held up

2 1 E 2 B 3 F 4 D 5 C 6 A

[3] Word order 1: noun objects

1 1 (a) Open the back of the camera and put the film in.
  (b) Open the back of the camera and put in the film.
2 (a) Don't throw the small container for the film away.
  (b) Don't throw away the small container for the film.
3 (a) Wind the film on until Number 1 appears in the window.
  (b) Wind on the film until Number 1 appears in the window.
4 (a) When you have finished, wind all the film back.
  (b) When you have finished, wind back all the film.
5 (a) Open your camera and take the film out.
  (b) Open your camera and take out the film.
6 (a) Send the film off to be developed and printed.
  (b) Send off the film to be developed and printed.

2 1 Will you put down the magazines which you're holding?
2 Will you pick up that magazine on the top of the pile?
3 Will you cut out the page with the big advertisement on it?
4 Will you hold up the advertisement on the page that you've just cut out?

3 Something caught Katie's attention.
        down   up
She bent / and picked / a small envelope addressed to her sister. She saw a wooden seat nearby and
        down   out
sat /. Then she decided to find / what was inside the envelope. She opened
        in   in
it, put her hand / *or* put / her hand and felt something small and hard.
                        out
She slowly took / a shining object. It was a gold watch! *or*
                                out
She slowly took a shining object / . It was a gold watch!

[4] Word order 2: pronoun objects

1 1 He's picking it up.
2 He's blowing it up.
3 She's taking them off.
4 He's putting it out.
5 He's filling it in.
6 She's sending them out.
7 She's buttoning it up.
8 He's handing them out.

2 B: Yes, Tom picked it up.
B: He put it down somewhere.
B: He probably took it out to use it.
B: It must have fallen out.
B: I hope no one has taken it away.

3 1 He tore it up.
2 She tried it on.
3 They locked him up.
4 She spat it out.

[5] Particles and prepositions

                        with
First, fill an electric kettle / water
        in
and plug it /. Next get a teapot and
                out
rinse it / with hot water from the
                        in
kettle. Then put a tea-bag / the teapot. As soon as the kettle boils,
        off
switch it / and pour the boiling
        in
water / the teapot. After a few
                with
minutes fill your cup / tea, put some
        in   down
milk and sugar / if you like, sit / and
        for
enjoy your tea. Don't wait / anyone or your tea will get cold!

2 1 You can write on it.
2 You should cross it out.
3 You shouldn't copy them out.
4 Don't try to rub them out.
5 You should cross them out.
6 You should/can cross out a whole sentence.
7 You can bring them into the room.
8 You cannot look at them.

[6] Revision 1

1 1 (a) Someone has taken away the television.
  (b) I wonder who has taken it away.
2 (a) Someone has pulled out one of the wires.
  (b) I wonder who has pulled it out.
3 (a) Someone has just brought back the CD I asked for.
  (b) I wonder who has just brought it back.
4 (a) Someone has torn out the last two pages of the book.
  (b) I wonder who has torn them out.
5 (a) Someone has now taken down the painting the committee didn't like.
  (b) I wonder who has taken it down.
6 (a) Someone has rubbed out the instructions the teacher wrote on the blackboard.
  (b) I wonder who has rubbed them out.

2 1 bring on 2 brought up 3 bring round 4 bring in 5 brought round 6 bringing in 7 bring out 8 bring off

3 Dear Wendy
I am sorry I missed you yesterday. I
        up
didn't get / until nine o'clock and,
                off
although I set / from home at half past nine, you had left when I
                                for
arrived. I do hope you didn't wait / me. I am very disappointed because I
                to   at
wanted to talk / you and look / your old photographs.
                        with
To make matters worse, I took / me some of my own photographs but I lost them on the way to meet you. I
        at
was looking / them on the bus and I
                down/away
remember putting them / when I
                        out
opened my purse and took / my

out
money *or* took my money / to pay my
fare. Someone must have seen my
              up
photographs and picked them /. I
only hope they haven't thrown
   away
them /. I look forward to getting a
        from
letter or phone call / you soon.
Love,
Mary

7 In, out

1
1 A 2 B 3 A 4 B 5 A 6 B
7 B 8 A

2
1 hand in 2 brought/gave in
3 pour/come 4 given/handed in
5 send out
All kinds of things have been handed
in at lost property offices. Recently a
small elephant was brought in. Every
day hundreds of enquiries come/pour
in about articles which people have
lost or mislaid (*or* about articles
which have been lost or mislaid). If
the articles concerned have not been
given/handed in, descriptions will be
sent out by the lost property office to
all the other lost property offices in
the area.

3
1 sent out 2 given/handed out
3 come/pour in 4 sent in 5 given/
handed/brought in

8 Off, on 1

1
1 come off 2 sew on 3 broken/
come off 4 stick on 5 pulled off
6 screw on 7 taken off 8 put on
9 stay on 10 tie on

2
1 it off 2 it on 3 it was turned/
switched on 4 them off 5 that
they were turned off
6 leave it on 7 switch them off/
leave them on 8 leave the oven on/
leave it in 9 turn it on 10 leave it
on

9 Off, on 2

1
1 got on 2 take off 3 try on
4 help on 5 Leave on 6 pull off

2
1 put off 2 call off 3 cut off
4 break off 5 let off

3
1 cut off 2 call off 3 put off
4 let off 5 broken off

10 Down, up 1

1
1 put down 2 picked up
3 walk up 4 bent down
5 sat down 6 stand/straighten up
7 bent down 8 sit down

2
1 taken down 2 put up 3 bend
down 4 pick up 5 stand up

3
1 His car has probably broken down.
2 He was brought up by his
grandmother.
3 It will be pulled down.
4 I feel (rather) let down.
5 No, he was making it up/making up
a story.
6 I shall probably turn up.

11 Down, up 2

1
1 gone up 2 come down
3 brought down 4 put up
5 forced down

2
1 down 2 down 3 up 4 down
5 up 6 down 7 up 8 up, up

3
1 shot up 2 came down 3 crept
up 4 stepped up 5 forced down

4
(Suggestion) The number of TV sets
sold since 1984 crept up steadily for
almost three years. However, the sale
of TV sets then came down until the
end of 1990 although the fall from
1989 to 1990 was so small that it was
scarcely discernible. In the following
year sales shot up as a result of a new
sound system together with price
reductions on most models. Since
then, sales of TV sets have crept up
steadily.

12 Up 1

1
(Suggestions)
1 He is waiting/staying up to watch
the match on TV.
2 The boy isn't up yet.
3 He knows that it's time to get up.

2
1 tore up the letter 2 dig up the
road 3 cut up the cardboard
4 divide it up 5 chopping up wood
6 broke up

3
1 walked up 2 ran up 3 drove up
4 come up

4
1 (a) Tie the parcel up with string
before you post it.
(b) Tie up the parcel with string
before you post it.
2 (a) Take a key so that you can
lock the equipment up before
you leave.
(b) Take a key so that you can
lock up the equipment before
you leave.
3 (a) It's very wet. Why don't you
button your raincoat up?
(b) It's very wet. Why don't you
button up your raincoat?
4 (a) Tighten the screws up before
you put the plug back in the
socket.
(b) Tighten up the screws before
you put the plug back in the
socket.

13 Revision 2

1
1 1 cut off 2 turn it on 3 broken
down 4 get out
2 5 let off 6 make up
3 7 let down 8 turn up 9 tore up
4 10 shot up 11 forcing up
12 bring down

2
   woke
I / up as soon as I heard someone
knocking on the door. As soon as I
            in
opened it, two men rushed /. One of
the men put his hand in his pocket
   took/pulled
and / out a small ring. 'That's Ben's,'
          down
I cried as I bent / and looked at it. 'A
strange old woman gave it to me,' he
said. 'I don't believe you. You're
         up
making it /,' I cried before running to
      up
pick / the phone. I dialled and began
          cut
to speak. But suddenly I was / off.
One of the men had put his hand on
            pulled
the phone while the other had / a gun
out and was pointing it at me.

3
(Suggestion) Liana was so tired
yesterday morning that she didn't
wake up when her alarm went off at
half past six. In fact, she didn't get up
until ten past eight. On her way to
work, she was held up in heavy
traffic, and then a wheel of her car
came off. After she had put it back
on, her car broke down! Later, when
she had managed to repair it, she had
to wait as some workmen were
digging the road up. She then began
to drive very quickly until a
policeman saw her and made her
slow down.

14 Away, off, out

1
1 I can't. He's driven off/away.
2 No, it flew away.
3 It's run away/off.
4 Throw it away.
5 They're taking it away.
6 No, they've gone away.

2
1 put out 2 blow out 3 put out
4 go out 5 went out 6 blow out

3
1 clean/clear 2 empty 3 get
4 clean 5 cleared

15 Off, out, up, on

1
1 dozed off 2 used up 3 killed off
4 dried up 5 tired out 6 finished
off
1 E 2 C 3 F 4 B 5 A 6 D

2
1 He dropped out after a few weeks.
2 He usually gives up.

3 Keep on trying even when something is very difficult.
4 No, because he carries on doing what he wants.
5 They want him to stay on at school.

3 (Suggestion) Beatrice Lee has hurt two fingers on her right hand but, in spite of this, she keeps on practising the piano every day. She started taking piano lessons five years ago and has never missed a lesson. She says that she has no intention of giving up now even though her two fingers are in bandages. Her piano teacher said she ought to try to play more with her left hand and rest her right hand. She finds this very difficult but she is trying hard not to carry on playing all her pieces with both hands.

16 About, around, round, over

1 (Suggestions) 1 running about 2 wandering about 3 standing about 4 lying around 5 throwing about 6 kicking around
(*Note that 'around' can be used in place of 'about' in nos 1, 2, 3 and 5, while 'about' can be used in place of 'around' in no 6.*)

2 (Suggestions) 1 She is offering some chocolate round.
2 She is handing cups of coffee round. 3 They are passing the photographs round. 4 He is taking the newspapers round.

3 (Suggestions) 1 I'll drive round now if you like. 2 Shall I cycle round now? 3 I'll hurry round now. 4 Yes, I'll wander round tomorrow. 5 Yes, I'll bring them round this week.

17 Down, off

1 1 let you down 2 pull it off 3 hit it off (with them) 4 pay off 5 come off 6 putting him down 7 turned me down 8 showing off

2 1 pull down 2 paid off 3 broke down 4 pulled off 5 came off 6 turned down
1 C 2 F 3 B 4 E 5 D 6 A

3 pulled off

18 Out, to

1 1 He tries to knock him out.
2 You might pass/black out.
3 They make sure that he/she comes round/to *or* they come round/to.

2 1 iron out 2 have out 3 sort out 4 turn out

19 Up 2

1 1 looking up 2 cropped up 3 blown up 4 put up 5 picks up 6 held up 7 thought up 8 making up

20 Three-word phrasal verbs

1 1 put up with such behaviour/it
2 face up to the problem/it
3 got on with Tom/him
4 got away without being punished/got away with not being punished
5 boils down to a demand for higher wages/boils down to that
6 get down to revising/it
7 go back on the promise you made to the children/your promise/it
8 have done away with the death penalty

2 (Suggestions)
1 The hotel has come in for a lot of criticism.
2 Perhaps Mr Brown will get round to cutting the grass one of these days.
3 I'm really looking forward to getting home.
4 The school has done away with uniforms.
5 Mary has gone in for a lot of competitions.
6 A burglar's made off with the TV set.

21 People

1 1 dropped in 2 take me out 3 bumped/run into him 4 looking forward to 5 pick me up 6 got on well (together)

2 1 on with 2 out 3 into, up 4 in, out, round/out 5 up, out 6 round, forward to, round 7 round, in 8 out

22 Food

1 1 dropped in 2 rustle up 3 take out 4 pour in 5 sat down 6 jumped up 7 boil over 8 put in 9 cut up/chop up 10 chop up/cut up 11 dish out/up 12 tuck in

2 (Suggestions)
1 I would advise them to cut out fatty foods as well as butter, cream and milk.
2 Try to cut out food containing a lot of fat, especially butter and cream.
3 I would tell them to cut down on the amount of food they eat, especially butter, milk, sugar, bread and rice.
4 You eat far too much. Why don't you cut down on bread, potatoes and rice? And don't put so much butter on your bread.

3 1 eat/dine out 2 eat/dine in 3 rustle up 4 serve up 5 dig in 6 get through 7 cut down on 8 wolf down

23 Health

1 1 down 2 out 3 out 4 up 5 out 6 up 7 down with 8 in 9 off 10 on

2 (Suggestions)
1 Why don't you sit down and have a glass of water?
2 Lie down and I'll get you a cup of tea.
3 Keep warm and stay in bed for a day.
4 Go to the doctor's and have a check-up.

3 (Suggestion) For cold sweats, nausea, and faintness. Do not drive or use machinery as it may make you sleepy. For a headache or stomachache, take one teaspoonful after meals until the pain has passed/been relieved. If the pain does not pass, or if you still feel sick, see a doctor as soon as possible. This medicine is not intended for people who constantly feel very tired or who are recovering from a serious illness.

24 Travelling

1 1 down, out, up 2 on 3 down, down, on, over/up, up, on 4 out, out, on, off 5 on, down, in, up 6 up, up, through, down, on

2 1 set off 2 check in 3 see off 4 take off 5 held up

25 Telephoning

1 1 look up 2 phone/ring up 3 put through 4 Hold on 5 cut off 6 Put down 7 get through 8 rung off

2 1 C 2 A 3 D 4 B

3 1 put you through
2 are through
3 rang her up
4 get through to her
5 cut us off
6 hung up/rang off
7 held on
8 ring me back

26 Police and crime

1 1 done in/bumped off 2 bumped off/done in 3 did out of 4 give up 5 went for 6 made off with

2 (Suggestions)
1 Someone is holding some people up in a bank.
2 A young man is making off with a lady's handbag.
3 A burglar is breaking into a house.
4 Several prisoners have broken out of gaol by climbing over a high wall.

3 1 look into 2 went for 3 let off, get off 4 broke into, made off with
1 C 2 B 3 D 4 A

27 Feelings

1 1 flared up 2 fed up 3 taken aback 4 cheered up 5 breaking down 6 let down

2 Simon and I used to [1] get on well with each other, but then Simon [2] fell out with Sarah. Simon had never [3] taken to/got on with Sarah, and he started to [4] put her down whenever he was with me. Eventually, Simon and I quarrelled, too. Some time later, however, Simon slowly [5] warmed to/took to/fell for Sarah and she also began to [6] take to/warm to/fall for him. They soon [7] struck up a close friendship, and Sarah stopped seeing me. I now feel very [8] cut up about the whole matter.

3 (Suggestions)
1 Always keep calm and don't get carried away when someone annoys you.
2 Don't let things get on top of you. Things will get better.
3 Why don't you change your job and apply for something more interesting?
4 Keep calm. It's only a game.
5 Cheer up. I'm sure your friend didn't mean to annoy you.

28 Revision 3

1 1 Does Helen get on with Anna/her, too?
2 Can Miss Tay put a student/one of the students up, too?
3 Did Harry Smart give himself up (to the police), too?
4 Did Ken hang up when he heard Sue's/her voice, too?
5 Was Rikako's train held up (for over an hour), too?
6 Did Hassan run into Spiros/Angelica (there/in the supermarket), too?

2 1 run down 2 blacked out 3 came to 4 check-up 5 gone up 6 cut out 7 come down with 8 face up to

3 (Suggestion) Harry Sharp was going for a drive the other day when he pulled up at a petrol station. After a petrol attendant had filled up his car with petrol, Harry set off and then pulled out into the middle of the road to overtake another car. Harry was going so fast that he couldn't stop at some traffic lights ahead. He went straight through even though the lights were at red. Unfortunately for Harry, a policewoman who was standing lower down the road had seen him and held out her hand for him to stop. However, Harry didn't take any notice and drove on. Eventually a police car chased Harry and caught up with him. Poor Harry didn't know what to do when a policeman got out and began to talk to him. 'I'm very sorry,' Harry said. 'I tried to drive through the amber lights and I just didn't see the policewoman. I'm on my way to see a friend who is very ill in hospital.' 'Well, I'll let you off with a warning this time,' the policeman said, 'but never drive like that again.'